Contents

Forms

Appendices

INTRODUCTION

See What I Mean is a set of guidelines which aims to help staff to question and check out or validate the accuracy of the meanings they ascribe to the communication of service users, particularly in the context of decision making. The guidelines involve:

1 A set of procedures for *gathering information and considering* the likely preferences of a person with a learning disability;

2 A set of procedures for arranging *a formal discussion* with a person with a learning disability to discover their wishes;

3 A set of procedures for *checking* interpretations.

● **Who are these guidelines for?**

The guidelines are intended for use by people who live and work alongside people with severe and profound learning disabilities, including:

Staff in day centre and residential settings
Teachers and learning support assistants in schools and colleges
Speech and language therapists
Advocates
Hospital staff
Managers
Policy makers who are planning service provision

● **When might you use these guidelines?**

In key decision making situations which involve service users
Annual reviews of the interests, wants and needs of service users
Transition – changes of environment, moving house, changing keyworker
In planning for self-advocacy with service users
Evaluation or appraisal of staff practice
Induction of new staff
Life events which demand careful examination of the views and feelings of service users, such as bereavement, hospitalisation, sexual relationships
Risk assessment

The guidelines do not substitute for formal procedures which are essential in legal settings, such as consent procedures or criminal proceedings, although the information can be used to support or complement findings which have legal status.

There are several reasons why we feel these guidelines are important:

● **Empowerment**

Services for people with learning disabilities are increasingly concerned with issues of empowerment, and government directives emphasise the importance of user involvement. This means that as far as possible, decisions and choices are made by service users, with staff acting in support of their clients. However, this is only likely to be achieved if service users have ways of communicating their wishes and feelings to staff who are able to interpret them.

● **The needs of people with severe and profound learning difficulties**

Services are providing for large numbers of people with very severe and profound learning difficulties and disabilities, many of whom do not speak and use few, if any, formal signs or symbols. Sometimes we may feel quite confident that we know what service users are communicating. However, there are other times when we are less sure, or where different people connected with the person are interpreting their communication in different ways. This is especially likely with individuals who do not have a vocabulary of words, signs or picture communication systems, but rely on facial expression, gestures, vocal sounds or other nonverbal behaviours. People with severe disabilities are likely to be highly dependent on others to interpret and support their communication. Recent research suggests that it is very difficult for staff who are working in busy environments to make accurate assessments of the level of sensory impairments among service users, or how much they understand what is said. This means that competence may be either under estimated or overestimated, leading to inevitable misunderstandings and misinterpretations.

● **Acquiescence**

The term "acquiescence" refers to the tendency of people with learning disabilities to agree with what is proposed to them. On the whole, they are more likely to say *yes* than *no* to a proposed course of action. They may also find it difficult to correct misunderstandings, because they do not really understand what is going on, or they lack the skills needed to contradict, or because they feel inhibited about doing so.

● **Conflicting assumptions**

When a decision has to be made about a person's lifestyle, there are likely to be many different agencies involved: family, carers, friends, advocates, doctors, therapists, teachers, key workers and social workers, to name but a few. Frequently, these agencies will have different perspectives on what the person needs, and it can be very difficult to know how much people are projecting their own interests, and how much the individual is contributing to an interpretation. It is important to recognise that such varied perspectives are natural to all human communication, and to be open and accepting about the differences.

- **Ambiguous authorship**

All communication results from the interaction of participants, who co-operate to construct messages and meanings in conversation. The level of support offered is likely to increase with the level of disability experienced by the person. When messages are produced with a high level of physical or vocal prompting, the ownership, or authorship, of a message may not be entirely clear. For example, Facilitated Communication is a strategy which involves physical support to allow a person to point to or touch objects, pictures or letters for communication purposes. The method generally involves the facilitator giving physical support, e.g. hand-on-wrist, or the stabilisation of a joint to enable movement of the arm. Although it is acknowledged that for some service users this method may indeed be helpful, there has also been much concern as to the ownership of the messages. There is now widespread recognition that, if communication is supported exclusively via the physical support of another person, the message which is apparently conveyed by the student/service user may actually be generated unconsciously by the communication partner. Hence it is vital to be scrupulous about checking whether the person with a disability communicates this information consistently – for example, to another person, and in other situations. Guidelines produced by the steering group for Facilitated Communication UK emphasise the importance of validation.

- **A way forward**

These issues may lead us to feel anxious about interpreting and responding to a person's apparent wishes, in case we have misunderstood her/his intentions. It is particularly difficult when significant decisions need to be made and a misinterpretation could have distressing and far-reaching consequences. However, although we cannot remove all the uncertainty which surrounds communication, we can develop some effective strategies for managing both the ambiguities and our anxieties about them. In *See What I Mean* we try to raise awareness of the problems, and to support staff in dealing with them.

THE NATURE OF COMMUNICATION

In order to become more confident and competent in relation to interpreting communication, it is important for staff to recognise and accept that they have a responsibility to be as accurate as possible in their interpretations of the communicative behaviours of service users. However it is a fact of life that all communication involves interpretation and guesswork – and sometimes we do get it wrong.

WHAT IS COMMUNICATION?

There are several ways of thinking about communication. One approach is to define it as a sort of code, with a message being encoded into signals by the speaker, and decoded for meaning by the listener. However, in practice this is too simple a view. Rather than seeing it as a package sent through the post which we "unpack" to find the meaning, we see it as a picture constructed by two or more people. The end result is a meaning – but what we need to identify is how that meaning has been built up, and who has contributed in what way. This puts the emphasis on the process rather than the product. This view of communication sees meaning and interpretations as dynamic, rather than static. Rather than there being one 'correct' meaning which the listener interprets either rightly or wrongly, meanings evolve in response to changing circumstances and will vary in relation to the differing perspectives of the individuals involved.

This is the case in all human communication – we are always reading things into what people say based on our knowledge of them, only getting part of the message right and misconstruing people's intentions. Sometimes we may correctly pick up signals about feelings that the speaker is not consciously intending to communicate. At other times we may think someone is communicating when they turn out to have been thinking of something else entirely. All communication involves some guesswork – based on our knowledge of others, we interpret what they do and say, and we quite often have to revise our first impressions. We are constantly guessing and checking up whether our guesses were right – but usually our communication partners are able to let us know if we are right or wrong.

INTENTIONAL COMMUNICATION

The guidelines are based on the view that all behaviour is potentially meaningful or communicative. We tend to react to all behaviours which we think tell us something about a person's inner state – such as yawns or head turns; but not all of these behaviours are necessarily intended to communicate messages to us. However, when behaviours are seen to be voluntary and purposeful, communication is said to be *intentional* – and we can then feel more confident that the person actively wants to tell us something, especially if meanings are communicated independently and persist when situations are varied. Figure 1 shows some of the commonest ways in which people show that they intend to communicate. It is difficult to be sure with people with very severe and profound learning disabilities, if their communication is intentional, and we must always therefore be prepared to ask how much the individual is actively contributing to the message.

Figure 1. Indicators of communicative intent

Alternating eye gaze: where a person looks at you, then at something or someone else, then back to you again.

Clear waiting for a response

Active seeking of proximity: a person moves to follow or sit close to someone

Systematic variation in behaviour: if you fail to respond, the person will repeat, elaborate or change the behaviour.

Persistence and intensity of behaviour: if a person repeats the same behaviour in different situations and with different people, and seems to do so forcefully.

These signals seem to indicate an awareness that other people are individuals and that you can enter into a dialogue with them. Infants seem to have this awareness almost from the start, but it is only around nine months that they begin to communicate explicitly that they want things from other people. As children acquire language, they are able to say specifically what they mean. Many people with severe and profound learning disabilities may never develop the ability to signal their intentions. Others may have the cognitive ability to do so, but their signals are hard to recognise because of physical or sensory problems. For example, eyegaze will not be used by people with severe visual impairments.

GUIDING PRINCIPLES

This view of communication leads us to adopt a particular set of principles when making decisions involving people with severe communication impairments:

- **Meanings are built co-operatively:**

All participants bring their own hopes and assumptions and experiences to the dialogue; these should be made explicit.

Example: *A parent may feel anxious about a son or daughter leaving home to live independently, and may be inclined to believe that they do not really want to go. The social worker may feel it is important for her service to show that people can move on, and may be inclined to think that the person does want to go.*

- **The contribution which the person with a learning difficulty can make to communication will vary with his or her level of understanding, communicative ability, interest and motivation.**

If a person can only communicate with a very high level of input from others, the meanings which are generated will probably only be valid with those people and in those situations. This is not to say that appropriate support should not be provided, but we must be sensitive to the fact that the more we assist someone's communication, the more likely we are to influence it, and the more rigorous our checks should be. The extent of support from other people must be specified fully.

Example: *A pencil is put in a child's hand, and his father holds a board on which the child's hand moves. The patterns that emerge are interpreted as writing by his father, who says "OK, you want to go to MacDonalds after school". However, no-one else can make out any letters. Since the writing can **only** be read by the person providing the support, the message which emerges is really only meaningful to his father.*

- **Meanings will be more generally valid if:**

- **they are communicated with clear intent**
- **they are communicated independently of physical support**
- **they persist when situations and partners are changed**

Example: *The person who looks at you, looks at the picture of the shops, vocalises, reaches towards the picture and then turns to the door, is giving clear signals of an intention or wish to go out that is not influenced by physical prompting.*

Example: *The person who moans and physically resists handling when it is time to sit in a particular wheelchair may just be feeling off colour. However, if she does it every time the chair is brought out, regardless of time of day, who is moving her, and her state of health, the interpretation that she dislikes this equipment is likely to be generally valid.*

- **An interpretation always represents a "best guess"; a hypothesis which needs to be checked and reviewed. Interpretations will vary; evidence must be provided in as full a form as possible to enable genuine and open discussion to take place.**

We should not be afraid of admitting that we are not sure what someone wants. These guidelines aim to help staff to explore interpretations of communication, by a careful structuring of the decision making situation, and by using strategies to check out possible meanings.

DECISIONS

THE NATURE OF DECISIONS

In everyday life, we are faced with hundreds of decisions: what to wear, whether to buy a paper on the way to work, whom to go out with, what job to do first from the pile on the desk. Some of these decisions are more important than others, and then we may want to sit down with friends or family and try to decide which course of action to take. Likewise, the choices which are made by people with learning difficulties will vary in their significance. We are not suggesting that the guidelines should be used every time you are unsure about what a person means, or every time they are involved in decision making. However, there will be some situations where it is important to check out the validity of the interpretations you are making about a person's wishes. There are several types of decisions, which vary in their significance to the individual, and to the community. Low significance decisions are those where a choice has to be made, but the outcome will not make a significant difference to the quality of life of the person concerned and will have little or no impact on other people. High significance decisions are likely to have a significant impact on the quality of life of the person concerned, and/or their families and friends. A hierarchy of decisions has been proposed by Ashton and Ward (1997).

1   Day to day living - *what to wear, where to go, whether to bathe. These are quite 'fail-safe'. - there is no risk of something going badly wrong for you if you make one decision or another. However, it can still be very important to get these choices right.*

2   Activities with a degree of risk - *going out alone, holidays, making friends, choosing a key worker. These are day to day choices which involve rather more uncertainty, but which are vital if people are to develop personal relationships and independence.*

3   Major life decisions - *where to live, who to marry.*

4   Major life decisions with legal implications - *serious medical interventions such as sterilisation; financial decisions such as claiming benefits or making wills.*

Decisions can be categorised according to their impact on an individual, and on society (Figure 2).

Be careful not to make too many assumptions about what kinds of choices are of high or low significance. What may, on the surface, appear to be of low significance, e.g. a choice between tea or coffee, may have greater meaning and importance for a student or service user than an issue of, apparently, higher long term significance. The framework is useful as a guideline for considering how much discussion and review needs to take place around the decision.

As a general rule we suggest that you may need to check the interpretations of decisions which are of high significance to individuals or families, friends and society.

Figure 2. Examples of different types of decision

	Society Low	**Society High**
Individual Low	Decisions may not be particularly important either to the individual or to society - **Example:** *Deciding which of two pairs of trousers to put on in the morning.*	Decisions may be highly important to society, but not to the individual. **Example:** *In a case brought about discrimination, the person themselves may not appear to be aware of what has happened, and may be more concerned with the quality of his next meal.*
Individual High	Decisions may be highly important to an individual, but have a low impact on the rest of society. **Example:** *Choice of key worker, or planning a birthday party.*	Decisions may be highly important to an individual and to society. **Example:** *Any cases with legal implications, such as adoption or allegations of harassment, discrimination or abuse*

DECISION MAKING PROCESS

At the point where a decision needs to be made, it may be possible to engage the individual in a meaningful review of the options available. Increasingly, people are present at their own case conferences and reviews, but if this is not to be tokenistic, you must be realistic about how much they understand and can actively participate in the process. In general, the more formal the situation the higher are the demands on a person's communication skills. *See What I Mean* provides a four-stage model to support decision making, with a set of procedures to accompany each step (see Figure 3) The contexts range from naturalistic observation to structured discussion:

- **Information gathering**
- **Discussion**
- **Checking interpretations**
- **Summarising**

Information gathering (Form A)

We view information gathering as an important first step which should be used with all service users involved in significant decision-making. The form should be completed by one or two key people who are supporting the person concerned. The form is designed to build up a picture of the key issues involved in the decision, by making it clear what has to be decided, who is involved, and what different people are likely to think about the best course of action.

You may find that there is general agreement about these questions. In other situations, people may hold very divergent views. It is important to be honest and to recognise that there is often no right or wrong answer – we will just have to do the best we can on the evidence available. If there are disagreements, it may be useful to discuss the views of others, and to follow up with more systematic observation, such as a video of the person in a relevant context. For example, you might observe an interaction with the person in a new environment, and see what feelings appear to be shown.

Once this information has been gathered, and you have come to a conclusion about what the person is likely to want or need, there are two possible routes to follow. For some people, it would be inappropriate to try to engage them in a discussion about their wishes. In this case, you will need to proceed straight to the stage of checking your interpretations. For other people, however, it may be appropriate to go on and take part in a structured discussion or meeting in which you try to elicit their own views and feelings.

Discussion (Form B1, B2)

Some individuals may have the skills to be actively involved in a process of discussion. To do this properly will require some preparation in which you take account of the best way to help the person benefit from the situation. Form B1 is a preliminary checklist designed to help you *plan* a discussion with a person with learning difficulties in ways which will minimise the risks of mis-interpretation. Form B2 is a follow-up checklist designed to help you *evaluate* the discussion. We suggest that it is recorded in some way, so that it can be reviewed independently if necessary. At the end of the form is a space to record your interpretation of the person's wishes. There are notes accompanying the checklist which explain some of the points more fully. You should keep a copy of any transcript or record along with the form.

Checking interpretations (Form C)

Once all the key people have been consulted, you will have gathered views which may support one *interpretation* of a person's wishes. However, it is important to think critically about the evidence on which you are basing your interpretations, and you should be aware of the possibility that other interpretations might be valid. You should attempt to check your interpretations by using some of the procedures suggested in Form C. In everyday life we check out what others mean by asking them directly, but also by observing their behaviour, by comparing what they say in one situation with another, and by consulting other people. We do this all the time – so all we are doing here is making more systematic and explicit use of our intuitive natural skills of communication.

- **Summarising and reviewing the process (Form D)**

Finally, the guidelines include a form for *summarising* the relevant information which has been gathered to support the decision. In most cases, it will be relevant to think about a review of the process at a later date. The process of summing up and reviewing ensures that everyone who participates has a clear view of what behaviours are regarded as communicative, and the meanings which are assigned to those behaviours.

These procedures may seem time-consuming. However, the time you put in at this early stage may well help to safeguard against mistakes and misinterpretations. Each step of an important decision can be made clear to those involved. The nature of the evidence base for one interpretation or another will be revealed.

SEE WHAT I MEAN PILOT STUDY

See What I Mean was piloted by 18 professionals, who included community nurses, speech therapists, day centre staff, a teacher and an advocate. They worked mostly in day services or residential centres (12) , some having contact with a few service users regularly, whilst others worked across community trusts (5) and came into regular contact with between 50 and 100 service users. All reported involvement in decision making with people who participated actively, in a limited way, or tended to be passive or disengaged, with few formal communication skills. All reported that they were likely to experience some conflicts of interpretation at different levels of decision making. After using *See What I Mean*, respondents commented that it provided a good model of practice, raised awareness, encouraged dialogue and reflection, and acted as a force against conflict. Personal and political views were highlighted through the process, and made available for analysis. The procedures were deemed to be flexible and a help in promoting individual rights and choices. Respondents provided specific comments about the wording, organisation and lay out of sections, which led to some minor changes in the format. The procedures were then re-piloted by three speech and language therapists. Details of the questionnaire used in the pilot study, sample case studies provided by respondents and an example of a completed form can be found in Appendix A and Appendix B.

Figure 3 **Decision making flowchart**

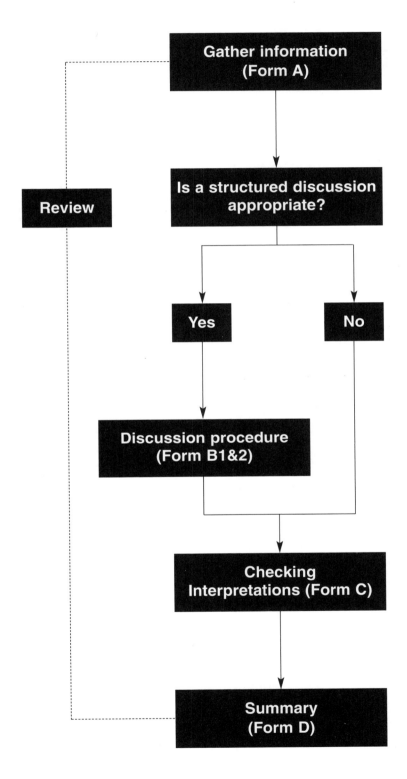

A Information Gathering

This form is designed to help you gather information to support the decision making process process - photocopy as required.

1. Describe the decision which needs to be made

....

....

What are the alternative courses of action you might take?

....

....

Is the decision to be made:

by the individual concerned? ☐ Yes ☐ No

on behalf of the individual concerned? ☐ Yes ☐ No

2. Is the person aware of the decision that needs to be made? ☐ Yes ☐ No
Does the person seem to have any views, attitudes or feelings relevant to the decision?

If so, please describe ....

....

....

3. Who are the other key people involved?

....

....

4. What is the range of views among key people involved in the decision?
about the best course of action, or about meanings or interpretations of behaviour

....

....

It is crucial that people feel able to be honest about their own wishes for the person with a disability. Any differences of opinion should be made explicit in as neutral a way as possible.

5. What evidence needs to be collected in order to come to a decision? Please describe.
eg. video of the person in different situations; presentation of information to the person;
profile of likes and dislikes; interviews with other people

Who will collect this information?

When will it be collected (dates)?

6. What level of participation in decision-making can be expected from the person?

- is likely to make an active contribution to the decision *Tick where*
eg. knows what he wants, understands something of the situation, *applicable*
and can consistently express some negative and positive views

☐

- is likely to participate in a limited way
eg. can indicate preferences when shown pictures of people and places
can indicate what s/he does not like

☐

- is likely to be a passive observer only
eg. may smile and react to the presence of others, but may not
appear to understand much of what is going on

☐

- is likely to disengage from the process
eg. withdraws, engages in stereo-typical behaviour

☐

7. What process will you use to reach the decision?

Consider which of the following is most appropriate and relevant to the needs, wishes and abilities
of the person concerned. It may be of value for the person to be present during a discussion,
whatever their level of functioning, if it gives them a sense of inclusion.
However, it is important to be realistic about the degree of their involvement. *Tick where*
applicable

- a structured discussion with the person ☐

- a structured discussion where the person is present, but has minimal involvement ☐

- a discussion where the person is not present ☐

- other (*please describe*) ☐

You should now have a clear idea about the nature of the decision; the views of the people
involved; the evidence you need to collect, and the process you will use to reach the decision.

B1 Discussion Checklist

This form is designed to help you plan a discussion where the person with a communication impairment will be present. Refer to the notes for factors which should be taken into account. Photocopy as required.

1 THE DISCUSSION

1.1   Date of discussion   Time: *from*   *till*

Place   Who will be present

How will the discussion be recorded?
(written record only; tape recording; video recording)

1.2   Purpose of discussion

1.3 What information has already been given to the person concerned about the event/decision

what?

by whom? *(specify named person)*

when? *(specify date)*

2   THE PERSON WITH A COMMUNICATION IMPAIRMENT

2.1 Medical factors likely to affect the discussion *(eg. drug regime)*

2.2 Are any adaptations needed to take account of sensory impairments? ☐ Yes ☐ No

Adapt for visual impairment by:

Adapt for hearing loss by:

Adapt for physical disabilities by:

Tick where applicable

2.3 Level of understanding in typical everyday situations

- appears unimpaired *(eg. can follow a complicated conversation)* ☐

- some difficulties with complex language ☐

- understands simple sentences ☐

- understands only single words ☐

- seems to understand only tone of voice ☐

- we do not know how much the person understands ☐

2.4 Level of intentional communication in typical everyday situations

- can reliably communicate information about an event to someone who was not there ☐

- can communicate information but only when the context is familiar ☐

- communicates intentionally using some of these strategies ☐

☐ *looking at something, then looking at you*
☐ *gestures eg reaching, pointing*
☐ *changing behaviour to try to make you understand what is wanted*
☐ *purposeful movement to find or be near someone/something*
☐ *persistent behaviour*
☐ *other strategies (please describe)*

- does not seem to communicate intentionally ☐

15

2.5 Means of expression *(Note all the ways in which the person communicates)* *Tick where applicable*

- uses speech ☐

- uses sign ☐

- uses communication aid *(specify which one)* ☐

- uses communication book or chart *(please indicate how aids, books and charts are used – eg eye, finger or hand pointing, switch use etc)*

....

....

- Can the person reliably and consistently indicate yes? *(please describe)* ☐ Yes ☐ No

....

....

- Can the person reliably and consistently indicate no? *(please describe)* ☐ Yes ☐ No

....

....

- Can the person reliably and consistently indicate positive or negative feelings? *(please describe)* ☐ Yes ☐ No

....

- What kind of information does the person recognise? *Tick where applicable*

- can recognise written words ☐

- can recognise symbols ☐

- can recognise pictures ☐

- can recognise objects of reference ☐

2.6 How do you think the person feel about the discussion?
eg. *interested, aware, confident, nervous, unaware, uninterested, angry...*

....

....

3 PARTNERS' COMMUNICATION
The term partner refers to the person who will mainly be involved in organising the discussion

3.1 Level of support
Are there any strategies you need to use to help and encourage the person to interact? Please describe (*eg. pausing to allow time to respond; seating positions; any physical support provided to prompt selection of objects/pictures/symbols/words, or to prompt manual signing*).

3.2 Specify in advance your most important questions and how you will ask them.
yes/no questions; open-ended questions;

3.3 Specify the main resources you will use to help the person understand what is involved eg. *signs, symbols, photographs*

3.4 What key words (*spoken, in sign, in symbols, pictures or objects*) will you need to use to convey the information?

Do you know if the person already understands these concepts? ☐ Yes ☐ No
How do you know?

4 Any other information needed to plan for the discussion

You should now have a clear idea about how to organise the discussion. Use form B2 to record what happened.

B2 Results of Discussion

Use this form to record details of the discussion. Photocopy as required

Date of discussion

Who was present?

Brief summary of key points from discussion

How was the discussion recorded? *Attach a written transcript or record, and a note about the location of any video or audio recording*

If the person with a communication impairment was present during the discussion, please complete the following:

1 What information do you think the person understood?

What is your evidence?

2 What do you think the person was communicating to you?

3   What was the level of participation in discussion? *(tick one only)*

- made an active contribution to the decision *(give an example)* ☐

- participated in a limited way *(give an example)* ☐

- was a passive observer ☐

- disengaged from the process ☐

Examples

---

4   So far as you can tell, was the response:

- typical of the person's usual pattern of communication ☐

- better than usual ☐

- poorer than usual ☐

---

5   Was any support provided to help the person communicate?

• physical prompting
Full physical prompt *(eg. the person's hand was guided to point to a picture)* ☐

Some level of physical prompt *(eg. touch on arm to prompt point or sign)* ☐

• verbal prompting
You spoke, signed or pointed a response, which the person imitated. ☐

• other *(specify this)* ☐

---

6 Were there any indications that the person was communicating intentionally?
What were they?

You should now be clear about what happened in the decision making process and be ready to consider your interpretations.

Discussing Decisions with People with Severe Communication Impairments

•Time

Think about when it will be best to have a discussion with somebody, in relation to when they will be at their most alert and communicative. Take into account: drug regimes; diet and eating habits (make sure people are neither hungry or thirsty, nor full and sleepy after a meal); body clocks (some of us are "morning" people and some of us are "afternoon" people), routines (don't start an interview when transport is due to arrive). Make sure you give yourselves enough time for the discussion - you can always finish early. For significant discussions, agree times with the person concerned - make sure that the date and time you decide does not clash with events which are important to the person, or others who may need to be there.

•Place

Where you choose to hold the discussion will be affected by its purpose. Generally speaking, we are all better at communicating in relaxed and familiar surroundings. We may also adapt to the context we are in and the expectations this puts on us. If I am having a discussion at work, I may give the sort of answers I think are appropriate to "me as an employee" or "me as a career woman" compared to the answers I might give at home "me as a mum". If there is a reason for holding an interview in unfamiliar surroundings, it may be worth putting the discussion off until the person has had a chance to visit the location once or twice. For significant discussions, decide the location with the person concerned.

•People present

Think about who should be present at the discussion. For important discussions, the person may wish to have a friend, family or staff member present, and to choose who this will be. In other situations, a neutral observer may be preferred. Again, try to make sure this is somebody whom the person has met and seems to respond to, since the presence of unfamiliar people can be very inhibiting to good communication. Discuss who will be present with the person concerned, and make sure they are introduced in the meeting.

•Recording method

All discussions which are to be used as the basis for significant decision making should ideally be video-recorded, and transcribed, so that it is possible to review the process. The transcription should record exactly what was said, and as far as possible, exactly what the person with a learning disability said or did. Of course, everyone is so busy that it may not be possible to do a detailed transcription - but video evidence will be extremely useful as a reference point, especially in situations of conflicting agendas. In discussions which are deemed to be of only minor significance, a simple written record may be kept. It is sensible to try to agree the broad content as an accurate record with those concerned - for example, at the end of the meeting.

•Purpose

What is the reason for the discussion? State this clearly, to help you think through where it should be held, who should be present, and what issues should be raised.

●Prior information

Think about how to present the discussion to the person concerned. What information needs to be given to the person beforehand, if any? How will this information be presented, taking into account the person's level of understanding and expression?

●Organising the environment

Think about how best to position the person, and yourself, taking into account any difficulties with sight, hearing or physical movements. If the person is using a communication board or device, or needs to have pictures or objects presented, make sure he or she is in the right position to be able to see and use these appropriately.

●Organising your communication

Think about how you will communicate with the person. Do you need to use signs, and/or to point to symbols or pictures to illustrate what you are saying? What is the person's level of understanding? level of intent? means of expression?

●Organising the questions

Try to decide beforehand what questions you will ask, in what order. Take into account the person's level of understanding - you may need to discuss how to phrase questions with a speech and language therapist.

There are two types of question:-
i. *Yes-No Questions* require only "yes" or "no" as response.
eg. "Can you?" "Do you...?" "Will you...?" "Have you...?"

Your questions should aim to elicit both positive and negative responses, and you need to be aware that if someone always seems to agree (or disagree!) this may indicate a difficulty in understanding, rather than a genuine response. Remember that people are likely to agree passively to suggestions, and that they may have a tendency to choose the last option offered, because it is the one they recall most easily - not because it is what they really want. For example a question such as "Would you like Mary as your keyworker, or Simon?" is likely to elicit "Simon". It may be better to present photographs of alternative people and see if a choice can be made.

Be careful about the ordering of yes-no questions - vary them and make sure you are not asking yes and no alternately; all one type followed by all the other type.

ii. *Open-ended questions* These require something other than "yes" or "no", and typically involve question words such as "What? Where? Who? When? Why? How?"

"What/Where" questions are understood earlier and more easily than the more abstract "When/Why/How" type.

People who have limited language skills must have the means to answer open-ended questions available to them, ideally in the form of pictures, symbols, real objects or people. Even people who appear to speak or sign well may benefit from a collection of photographs or symbols relevant to the discussion topic, since this will help their memory for what they want to tell you. People with learning disabilities will experience particular difficulty with abstract concepts such as time, causation and consequences of decisions or actions. They may also find it hard to answer evaluative questions involving relative judgements such as "more" "better" "less". The "Talking Mats" approach (see resource list) may provide some ideas for organising questions.

Other points to note:

Questions should be as short and simple as possible. Try to use words that will be within the person's vocabulary. If you have to use unfamiliar words, provide picture or symbol cues, explain them, and make sure that you reinforce the teaching of these words after the discussion: you may need to repeat this question at a later point.

Each question should require only one answer (*not* - did you go to visit your new home, and how did you like it?)

Questions can be illustrated with symbols, pictures or objects of reference - but in this case, try make sure that the person recognises both the illustration and the meaning before you undertake the discussion.

You may need to repeat questions, either immediately or at points during the discussion as a check that the person has understood. Introduce checking explicitly:
"Can I just ask you this again, so I'm sure I know what you mean?"
"I'm going to ask you this question a few times, because I want to be sure what you're telling me".

Too much repetition will both confuse, and lead to inattention. Better to abandon the question if you cannot get a clear response, and make a note to explore the issue further, or ask it at another time.

- **Thinking about Responses**

Check whether the person has consistent ways of signalling yes and no, and what it is (eg. eye blink may mean "yes", head turn "no"). The checklist provides a space to indicate whether the person can always do this, sometimes do it, or do it only occasionally.

Also check whether the person has a tendency to always answer "yes" or "no".

For people who do not have a yes-no response, decide beforehand what you will regard as being positive, negative and neutral responses, through discussion with keyworkers, family and friends.

For answers to open questions, or for interpreting comments that the person may make, check how they respond to pictures, symbols or objects. Collect those that are relevant to the discussion topic. Note how the person "accesses" information, as above - through pointing, through eye gaze, through switching.

Check whether the person shows any response bias - that is, a tendency to produce the same response, no matter what the stimulus is. For example, a person may always look to the left side, or point to the object in the middle. Strong response biases may simply reflect the fact that the person is so physically disabled that only this movement is possible, but might also be due to over-reinforcement by caregivers and staff (it is very easy to be misled by a response bias). In the latter case, the person may not be making a genuine choice, and may not have understood what you are offering.

Check by presenting the stimulus at a different location. You should make the checking process explicit, eg. "You seem to be choosing the pictures on this side. Can we swap them around a bit, so I can be sure what you want to tell me?"

If the person responds ambiguously, you will need to explore this issue further outside the discussion context.

- **Pacing the discussion**
  Research shows that people with learning disabilities need time to formulate their thoughts and to communicate. Make sure you leave a long enough pause after a question or statement to give the person a chance to answer. Show that you expect an answer by making use of tone of voice, body posture and facial expression – lean forward, raise your eyebrows and gesture towards the person to indicate that it is now their turn.

  A barrage of questions is very off-putting. Make space during the discussion to:

  - introduce a topic, and talk around it a bit – for example by going through photographs together.
  - have a chat about something different, involving other people who are present.
  - have a drink, or a break to allow someone to change their position or come out of a wheelchair for a rest.

- **Alternative approaches**
  When working with people who cannot realistically take an active role in decision making, you may wish to consider alternative ways of discovering and representing their perspectives. For example, The Nottinghamshire Interagency Strategy for people with severe learning difficulties, organised a consultation with service users to discover what they felt made a "good day" or a "bad day". Members of the Joint Commissioning Team 'shadowed' service users with profound and multiple learning difficulties in order to observe their experiences at first hand (See Money & Collins 1999).

C Checking Interpretations

1 What interpretation has been made about the person's wishes and feelings regarding the decision which has been taken?

_____

_____

2 What other supporting evidence is there for this interpretation?

Tick where applicable

- the person can communicate the same meaning to others who have no knowledge of the decision ☐

- discussions with other people suggest that the interpretation is valid ☐

- observations of the person's behaviour in other situations suggests the interpretation is valid *(please specify)* ☐

_____

_____

- we are unsure about the validity of the interpretation ☐

3 Has this interpretation been elicited in any other situations?

- with the same partner *(please specify)* _____ ☐

- with a different partner *(please specify)* _____ ☐

- in a different setting *(please specify)* _____ ☐

- at different times *(please specify)* _____ ☐

4 Do other people agree with this interpretation? *(please specify any other views that are held by key people concerned)*

_____

_____

_____

5 Is there any evidence to support a different interpretation? *(please specify)*

6 Do you need to gather any further information or evidence to support the decision making process? ☐ Yes   ☐ No

If yes, what information will you collect?

Who will collect the information?

When will the information be collected by (date)?

D Summary

This form summarises key information about the decision, and the views and feelings of those involved. Photocopy as required

1 The user's wishes seem to be:-

....

....

2 What do other people want: *(complete as appropriate)*

Family   Advocate

Key workers   Policy makers

Friends   Other professionals

....

....

....

3 Provisional decision/course of action:

....

....

4 This interpretation will be monitored by:

....

....

5 How will the decision be reviewed?

....

....

6 Date for review:

....

Appendices

A: CASE STUDIES OF 'SEE WHAT I MEAN' IN PRACTICE

The following brief case studies were provided by respondents to the pilot study. They illustrate the use of the procedures with service users with different abilities, facing choices of varying significance in their lives.

JANE

● The individual

Jane is a lady with profound and multiple learning disabilities, who lives in a residential centre. She has no formal means of communication, and her level of understanding is very difficult to determine. She expresses positive feelings by smiling, and negative feelings by shrieking, rocking and hitting herself. She frequently withdraws from situations, and appears anxious and confused. Objects of reference are being introduced to help her to recognise experiences and to make choices; however, as yet she shows little recognition or reaction to these.

● The decision

Jane attends a hydrotherapy session regularly, which she seems to enjoy. However, she becomes very agitated and distressed in the course of the journey, which takes half an hour there and back. The choices involved were:

- to continue to attend the specialist centre
- to discontinue the visits
- to seek out opportunities locally, though this would have cost implications for Jane, who would have to pay for the facilities herself.

● Key people and their wishes

Staff from the home wanted the placement to continue, but were finding the journeys very difficult. Jane's named nurse wanted the placement to continue, and felt that local facilities were not suited to her physical and emotional needs. The physiotherapist wanted the placement to continue, as hydrotherapy contributes to her physical health and well being. The Social Services case manager felt staff should use the local pool, as it would deal with the problem of the journey time, and promote Jane's quality of life by increasing her contact with the community. Jane's parent wanted the hydrotherapy to continue.

● The discussion

The discussion took place in the centre, with Jane, a named nurse, her keyworker, the unit manager and the physiotherapist. A written record was kept of the proceedings. A swimming float was used as an object of reference to indicate the topic to Jane, but she took no notice of it, and appeared withdrawn throughout the conversation. This was felt to be typical of her reactions in these situations.

● Course of action

Since Jane always seems to enjoy the hydrotherapy session, the assumption was made that she would wish to continue. The provisional decision was to continue the current placement, looking at ways of cutting down the journey time - for example by travelling at a different time of day. At the same time, alternatives would be explored. The atmosphere at the local pool was felt to be very noisy and crowded, and staff felt it would be difficult to manage sessions therapeutically there - however, one possibility discussed was to involve local councillors and Mencap to look at changes which might be made.

The outcome

It was decided that the local community option was not feasible at the present time. Trips to hydrotherapy were continued on the basis that staff assessed Jane's mood each week. This resulted in attendance approximately 8/10 times. Only twice was there a need to curtail the journey. Transport seems to be the problem, but it is still not entirely clear what causes her such distress.

Comments

This case study illustrates the complexity of what on the face of it seems a relatively simple issue. The key people involved all have different views, motivated by a variety of considerations. For staff, their commitment to providing the appropriate service for Jane is undermined by the difficulty of getting her there, which is causing distress to everyone concerned. For the case manager, there is a political dimension – he mentioned the need to fulfil the Five Accomplishments, to which his service is committed, and his view was that this would best be achieved through inclusive rather than segregated provision. The fact that Jane would have to pay for a local facility raises the question of who owns the money, and who has the right to decide how it should be spent. The final discussion shows how a decision which at first is highly individualised begins to take on a wider social significance once the question of access to the local pool is considered.

The role of 'See What I Mean'

In this case, the use of the procedures enabled participants to be open about their own views and wishes, and to look realistically at the level of Jane's participation. Decisions which had been viewed as discrete – go to hydro or not? use local facilities or not? who pays? were recognised to be interlinked. *See What I Mean* also helped as a guide for alerting staff to things they might have forgotten.

SIMON

The individual

Simon is a man with severe learning difficulties, who has no formal means of communication. He lives at home with his parents, and attends a day centre. He makes negative feelings known by loud shouting, or by turning his head away. He is calm when doing things he likes such as eating, swimming, walking or having his hands massaged, which he will initiate by holding out a hand, and making eye contact. He tends to be a passive observer in discussions.

The decision

Simon has recently started to put his finger regularly to his mouth. The question is how to interpret and respond to the behaviour.

Key people and their wishes

Some staff at the day centre thought this was a request for a drink, and responded to the behaviour as such. Others thought it was stereotypical, self-stimulatory behaviour, which they should try to eliminate. His parents wanted the behaviour to stop because Simon's mouth was becoming sore.

The discussion

The discussion was held in the centre, between Simon's keyworker, the parents and the speech and language therapist. A written record was kept. The purpose was to view a video of the behaviour which had been taken in several situations. Simon himself was not present.

● Course of action

There was a consensus after viewing the video that the behaviour appeared to be self-stimulatory and random, rather than a request for a drink. It was decided to work to phase out the behaviour, and to review progress at Simon's forthcoming annual review. Interestingly, the analysis of the video helped to identify a more positive behaviour (leaning forward in his chair) which looked to be intentional.

● The outcome

Staff now respond to the leaning forward as a request to change position, and are looking for signs that Simon is beginning to associate his movement with their response.

● The role of 'See What I Mean'

This case study illustrates how easy it is in a busy centre for people to make quite different assumptions about the meaning of a behaviour, and thus respond to it in a variety of ways. This has the effect of reducing the consistency of experience for the individual, and can lead (as in this instance) to intermittent reinforcement, which may increase the likelihood of recurrence of the behaviour. The procedures allowed the key people to share their interpretations and to look objectively at evidence collected on video.

JOHN

● The individual

John is a man with severe learning difficulties who spent 30 years of his life in a long stay hospital. He now lives in a special unit for people with severe learning difficulties and challenging behaviour. He can understand simple sentences, and communicates through a few words and phrases. He can make choices from symbols or pictures. He indicates positive and negative feelings quite conventionally, through nodding and smiling, or shaking his head and frowning. Despite these good communication skills, it is not always clear what John wants from a situation. He can, however, participate to some extent in a discussion.

● The decision

A project was being launched locally to re-unite former residents of the hospital.
The choices for John were:
a) not to participate in the project
b) partial participation - not going on the visits
c) total participation, including the visits.

● Key people and their views

The key people involved were: John and his fellow residents, the Unit manager, the keyworker, the psychologist, the speech and language therapist and John's father. All staff felt the project was very positive, but were anxious that John should not feel pushed into doing it. Some worried that John might think he was going back to the hospital. There was some uncertainty as to whether a repeated phrase that John used "Jimmy Jones" (the name of a former resident) indicates that the two men were good friends, or whether it was stereotypic.

● The discussion

Discussion did not take place at a set time, since opportunities have to be taken to engage John in a conversation when he is interested and willing. Two members of staff discussed the project with him on several occasions, and a written record was kept. The purpose was to assess John's response to the suggestion of meeting up with old friends. Photos, video clips and a life book with pictures of the hospital were used, with questions such as "who is this?" and simple descriptions to John about the pictures.

Key words included "house; visit; see; Jimmy Jones; go for tea; friend" all concepts which John was known to understand in the context of everyday living, although it was not clear what "friend" meant to John. During the discussions, John participated in a limited way. He became animated, smiling and laughing when Jimmy Jones was mentioned, and he responded in the affirmative when asked whether a visit should be arranged.

● Course of action
Staff felt confident in their interpretation of John's wishes – he was consistent in his responses to different staff, at different times of the day. Contradictory evidence might be if John refused to enter or leave the bus on the day of the visit, or showed distress on meeting the group. It was agreed that the visit should go ahead.

● The outcome
The first visit took place, but had to be abandoned because John found it distressing to be in the minibus taking him to see his former friends. Staff quickly reconsidered the plans and agreed that it would be better to hold the reunion on John's territory. Hence a second visit was held in a room close to John's home. John was then free to come in and out as he pleased, and indeed chose to spend twenty minutes with the group.

● The role of 'See What I Mean'
In this case, staff were keen to participate in a project that seemed exciting and worthwhile. However, our view of what is enjoyable and valuable will not necessarily be shared by clients. Use of the procedures enabled staff to be scrupulous about checking that their enthusiasm was shared by John.

A Information Gathering

This form is designed to help you gather information to support the decision making process

1. Describe the decision which needs to be made

Does John wish to be involved in a 'Real Lives' project where he and fellow residents will be re-introduced to former residents of the long-term hospital where he spent 30 years

What are the alternative courses of action you might take?
a) not to be involved b) to be involved and go on visits
c) to be involved but not meet people

Is the decision to be made:

by the individual concerned? [✓] Yes [ ] No

on behalf of the individual concerned? [ ] Yes [ ] No

2. Is the person aware of the decision that needs to be made? [✓] Yes [ ] No
Does the person seem to have any views, attitudes or feelings relevant to the decision?

If so, please describe

John appears positive at the idea of meeting old friends

3. Who are the other key people involved?

John and fellow residents of unit for people with severe learning difficulties and 'challenging behaviour'. Manager of Unit, Keyworkers, Psychologist, Speech and Language Therapist and his Dad

4. What is the range of views among key people involved in the decision?
about the best course of action, or about meanings or interpretations of behaviour

All staff feel project is a positive one - but want to be sure that John's wishes are respected and he is not forced into actions he doesn't want to do. John himself is not always clear in expressing himself and his views. Concern from some that John might think he is being told he's going back to the hospital

It is crucial that people feel able to be honest about their own wishes for the person with a disability. Any differences of opinion should be made explicit in as neutral a way as possible.

5. What evidence needs to be collected in order to come to a decision? Please describe.
eg. video of the person in different situations; presentation of information to the person; profile of likes and dislikes; interviews with other people

Discussion with John about the Real Lives Project

Who will collect this information? Speech therapist

When will it be collected (dates) During the formal discussion of the project

6. What level of participation in decision-making can be expected from the person?

Tick where applicable

• is likely to make an active contribution to the decision
eg. knows what he wants, understands something of the situation, and can consistently express some negative and positive views [✓]

• is likely to participate in a limited way
eg. can indicate preferences when shown pictures of people and places can indicate what s/he does not like [ ]

• is likely to be a passive observer only
eg. may smile and react to the presence of others, but may not appear to understand much of what is going on [ ]

• is likely to disengage from the process
eg. withdraws, engages in stereo-typical behaviour [ ]

7. What process will you use to reach the decision?

Consider which of the following is most appropriate and relevant to the needs, wishes and abilities of the person concerned. It may be of value for the person to be present during a discussion, whatever their level of functioning, if it gives them a sense of inclusion. However, it is important to be realistic about the degree of their involvement.

Tick where applicable

• A structured discussion with the person [✓]

• A structured discussion where the person is present, but has minimal involvement [ ]

• A discussion where the person is not present [ ]

• Other (please describe) [ ]

You should now have a clear idea about the nature of the decision; the views of the people involved; the evidence you need to collect, and the process you will use to reach the decision.

2.2 Are any adaptations needed to take account of sensory impairments? [ ] Yes [✓] No

Adapt for visual impairment by:- N/A

Adapt for hearing loss by:- N/A

Adapt for physical disabilities by:- N/A

Tick where applicable

2.3 Level of understanding in typical everyday situations

- appears unimpaired (*eg. can follow a complicated conversation*) [ ]
- some difficulties with complex language [ ]
- understands simple sentences [✓]
- understands only single words [✓]
- seems to understands only tone of voice [✓]
- we do not know how much the person understands [ ]

2.4 Level of intentional communication in typical everyday situations

- can reliably communicate information about an event to someone who was not there [ ]
- can communicate information but only when the context is familiar [✓]
- communicates intentionally using some of these strategies [✓]
  - *looking at something, then looking at you* [✓]
  - *gestures eg reaching, pointing* [✓]
  - *changing behaviour to try to make you understand what is wanted* [✓]
  - *purposeful movement to try to find or be near someone/something* [✓]
  - *persistent behaviour* [✓]
  - *other strategies (please describe)* [✓]
- does not seem to communicate intentionally [ ]

B1 Discussion Checklist

This form is designed to help you plan a discussion where the person with a communication impairment will be present. Refer to the notes for factors which should be taken into account.

1   THE DISCUSSION

1.1 Date of discussion *5.7.99*   Time: *from 2.00 till 2.30*

Place *Centre*   Who will be present *Keyworker and SLT*

How will the discussion be recorded?
(*written record only; tape recording; video recording*) *written record*

1.2 Purpose of discussion
To access John's response to the suggestion of meeting old friends as part of the project

1.3 What information has already been given to the person concerned about the event/decision

what? *told that staff have visited Jimmy Jones' house and that he could too if he wants*

by whom? (*specify named person*) *Keyworker*

when? (*specify date*) *in informal conversations over the last week*

2   THE PERSON WITH A COMMUNICATION IMPAIRMENT

2.1 Medical factors likely to affect the discussion (*eg. drug regime*)
epilepsy - leading up and just after a fit John is very drowsy and uncommunicative

3 PARTNERS' COMMUNICATION
The term partner refers to the person who will mainly be involved in organising the discussion

3.1 Level of support
Are there any strategies you need to use to help and encourage the person to interact? Please describe. (*eg. pausing to allow time to respond; seating positions; any physical support provided to prompt selection of objects/pictures/symbols/words, or to prompt manual signing*).

Favourite staff members, relaxed quiet one-to-one with a cup of tea!

Following the lead he shows in terms of engagement

3.2 Specify in advance your most important questions and how you will ask them.
yes/no questions   open-ended questions
Do you want to see ... etc ?

What's this? (photos)

Mainly descriptive language to John with no direct questioning

3.3 Specify the main resources you will use to help the person understand what is involved
eg. signs, symbols, photographs
Photos, life-book (with photos of past living accommodation and of John and his friends), video clips

3.4 What key words (spoken, in sign, in symbols, pictures or objects) will you need to use to convey the information?

House, visit (see), Jimmy Jones, go for tea, friend

Do you know if the person already understands these concepts? [✓] Yes [ ] No
How do you know?
Yes in context of own living situation and familiar visits eg to see Dad.

Responds to requests to be involved in these trips. Not sure what concept of

'friend' means to him.

4 Any other information needed to plan for the discussion
- as mentioned in 3.3

You should now have a clear idea about how to organise the discussion. Use form **B2** to record what happened.

	Tick where applicable

2.5 Means of expression (*Note all the ways in which the person communicates*)

- Uses speech [✓]
- Uses sign [ ]
- Uses communication aid (*specify which one*) [ ]
- Uses communication book or chart (*please indicate how aids, books and charts are used - eg eye, finger or hand pointing, switch use etc*)
  Can indicate simple choices through selecting symbols from choice of 3

- Can the person reliably and consistently indicate yes? [✓] Yes [ ] No
  (*please describe*)
  nods, smiles, behaviour

- Can the person reliably and consistently indicate no? [✓] Yes [ ] No
  (*please describe*)
  shakes, facial expression, behaviour

- Can the person reliably and consistently indicate positive or negative feelings? (*please describe*) [✓] Yes [ ] No
  smiles, giggles, stock phrases, physical movements

	Tick where applicable

- What kind of information does the person recognise?
- Can recognise written words [ ]
- Can recognise symbols [✓]
- Can recognise pictures [✓]
- Can recognise objects of reference [ ]

2.6 How do you think the person feel about the discussion?
eg. interested, aware, confident, nervous, unaware, uninterested, angry...
variable dependant on mood.

When photos introduced - quite animated

B2 Results of Discussion

Use this form to record details of the discussion

Date of discussion 5. 7. 1999

Who was present? John, Keyworker, SLT, Psychologist

Brief summary of key points from discussion

Positive response from John. Visit to proceed

How was the discussion recorded? Attach a written transcript or record, and a note about the location of any video or audio recording

- see attached

If the person with a communication impairment was present during the discussion, please complete the following:-

1 What information do you think the person understood?
Most of concrete facts.

What is your evidence?
Mainly intuitive. Staff have learnt with John to constantly monitor and reflect on his understanding and constantly reinforce meanings throughout.

2 What do you think the person was communicating to you?
Seemed to be enthusiastic and excited when Jimmy was mentioned.
Positive to suggestion that he might like to visit - giving the 'go ahead' to arrange a visit

---

3 What was the level of participation in discussion? (tick one only)
- made an active contribution to the decision (give an example) ☑
- participated in a limited way (give an example) ☐
- was a passive observer ☐
- disengaged from the process ☐

Examples smiled, repeated 'Jimmy Jones' and laughed. Close involvement with photos and video

4 So far as you can tell, was the response:-
- typical of the person's usual pattern of communication ☑
- better than usual ☐
- poorer than usual ☐

5 Was any support provided to help the person communicate?
- **Physical prompting**
Full physical prompt (eg. the person's hand was guided to point to a picture) ☐
Some level of physical prompt (eg. touch on arm to prompt point or sign) ☐
- **Verbal prompting** ☑
You spoke, signed or pointed a response, which the person imitated.
- **Other** (specify this) ☑
Pictorial visual materials (photos and videos)

6 Were there any indications that the person was communicating intentionally? What were they? Yes. 1. Alternate gaze - photos/staff.
2. Purposeful behaviour - stayed close to staff, eye contact etc
3. Typical behaviour observed by staff previously

You should now be clear about what happened in the decision making process and be ready to consider your interpretations.

5 Is there any evidence would support a different interpretation? *(please specify)*

If John refused to get in mini-bus or leave it when he arrived or showed distress/withdrawal on meeting group (after initial introductions) assumption would be made that he wished to stop visit

6 Do you need to gather any further information or evidence to support the decision making process? ☑ Yes ☐ No

If yes, what information will you collect?

Observations of John meeting other groups of new people - does he find this enjoyable or stressful?

Who will collect the information?

Direct Care staff, co-ordinated by The Speech & Language Therapist

When will the information be collected by (date)

June 1999 (6 weeks time)

C Checking Interpretations

Use this form to describe and check out interpretations

1 What interpretation has been made about the person's wishes and feelings regarding the decision which has been taken?

John wishes to meet his old friends and seems excited at the prospect. Staff confident enough of this to wish to make further arrangements

	Tick where applicable
2 What other supporting evidence is there for this interpretation?	
• the person can communicate the same meaning to others who have no knowledge of the decision	☑
• discussions with other people suggest that the interpretation is valid	☑
• observations of the person's behaviour in other situations suggests the interpretation is valid *(please specify)* *Staff confident that his general communicative behaviour is consistent with past experience*	☑
• we are unsure about the validity of the interpretation	☐

3 Has this interpretation been elicited in any other situations?	
• with the same partner *(please specify)* *repeat discussion*	☑
• with a different partner *(please specify)* *different staff*	☑
• in a different setting *(please specify)* _____	☐
• at different times *(please specify)* *over several days*	☑

4 Do other people agree with this interpretation? *(please specify any other views that are held by key people concerned)*
Yes. Consensus agreement amongst staff.

D Summary

This form summarises key information about the decision, and the views and feelings of those involved.

1   The user's wishes seem to be
To meet up and re-establish contact with old friends now living in unit
12 miles away

2   What do other people want:- *(complete as appropriate)*
Family   Advocate
Key workers   Policy makers
Friends   Other professionals
All wish for this process to go well and taking risk assessments etc into

account to proceed with the 'Real Lives' project

3   Provisional decision/course of action
Individual visits to be arranged by mutual convenience between the

2 units

4   This interpretation will be monitored by....
Residential staff from both units throughout and outside scope of visits

5   How will the decision be reviewed?
After each visit in consultation with ethics group/multi-dis team as

deemed appropriate

6   Date for review   *Johns next review date - 15.9.1999*

B 'SEE WHAT I MEAN' PILOT STUDY

This appendix presents and discusses the results from the pilot study.

1.0 Contexts of decision making: The pre-course questionnaire

The *See What I Mean* procedures are based on various assumptions:
- that all service users are probably involved in making choices or decisions at some level
- that different strategies may be appropriate for service users at different levels of ability
- that difficulties are inevitable and should be made explicit
- that practice and procedures probably vary across services, and could benefit from some basic standardisation
- that there is a hierarchy of significance of decisions, which have different implications for practice

The aim of the questionnaire was to explore to what extent there really were issues to be addressed about decision making with service users in different contexts. If there were to be high levels of agreement that there were no problems, or evidence of very consistent approaches to practice, then the procedures could perhaps be simplified and reduced to a basic checklist. However, if this small survey found a lot of variation, and evidence of concern among practitioners about decision making within services, then the more in-depth approach which we advocate would seem to be appropriate.

Eighteen professionals who attended a one day workshop on *See What I Mean* completed the questionnaire. They included community nurses, speech therapists, day/residential centre staff, an advocate and a teacher. Respondents worked mostly in day services or residential centres (12+ 1 school), some having contact with a few service users regularly, whilst others worked across community trusts (5) and came into regular contact with between 50 and 100 service users. Not all respondents completed every question, so that in the following account, numbers sometimes total less than 18.

1.1 Size of services

Services ranged from small (<10 = 4) to large (>200 = 4 including community trusts).

1.2 Service users

The majority (17) of respondents worked regularly with caseloads of under 50 clients. Six respondents worked with fewer than 10 clients on a regular basis, and obviously had the opportunity to get to know them very well. One respondent, a speech and language therapist, worked with a caseload of over 200 clients.

Respondents were asked how many service users would show the characteristics which made them vulnerable to over-interpretation or under-interpretation: high dependence on others for communication; low or ambiguous awareness of intent, and/or comprehension levels; limited and inconsistent expressive communication; suggestibility and difficulty in contradicting statements made by others. All services catered for individuals with these characteristics, and all respondents worked regularly with such individuals.

1.3 Decisions

Respondents were asked how often in the course of their work they would be considering decisions at different levels of significance. All respondents considered everyday choices several times a week; 15 of the 18 were doing this several times a day. Respondents varied considerably in the extent to which they confronted choices which were likely to result in significant short or long term changes to people's lives. In the case of decisions relating to short-term change, this ranged from several times a week (4) to less than once a year (1), the majority being several times a year (8). Long term changes were faced once or several times a year for 4 respondents, and less than once a year for 9 respondents. However, 3 respondents said that they engaged with such decisions monthly (1) or weekly (2). Choices with legal implications arose once a year or less for 14 of the 18 respondents: however, 1 respondent dealt with these issues several times a month, and 2 several times a year.

1.4 Involvement of others

Respondents were asked to indicate their views on how likely it was that others would participate in the process of decision making (see Table 1).

Front line staff were highly likely to be engaged in everyday decisions, and choices with short term implications, but less likely to be involved in choices with long term or legal implications – 8 respondents (45%) thought it unlikely they would be involved in the latter. *Senior managers within the service*, as would be expected, were very unlikely to be involved in everyday decisions, but highly likely to be involved in choices with long-term or legal implications.

Parents or carers, by contrast, were more likely to be involved as the impact of a decision increased: however, there was clearly a lot of variation, since in 50% of cases they were very likely to be involved in everyday decisions, and one third of respondents felt parents were unlikely to be involved at almost any level of decision making. Interestingly, these respondents were as likely to be working in day as in residential services: there was obviously no simple correlation between involvement of parents and carers and place of residence of service users.

The involvement of *independent advocates* seems to be dependent on access. One third of respondents either left this section blank, said they did not know, or filled in "not likely" at every level of decision making, and 3 commented that provision was patchy. Advocates were most likely to be involved in decisions with legal implications.

Involvement of *speech and language therapists* (SLTs) was very patchy and showed no consistent trends. Participation seems again partly dependent on access, since one third of respondents ticked "not likely" at every level, or left the section blank, and again 3 respondents (not the same as those who commented about advocates) said that provision was poor or non–existent. However, in between 50 and 60% of cases, the involvement of SLTs was thought to be unlikely at every level. By contrast, other professionals, such as social workers, psychologists, GPs and solicitors, were more likely to become involved as the impact of a decision increased. In choices with long term or short term implications, over 80% of respondents thought they were quite likely or very likely to be involved.

Respondents were asked how often there would be substantial differences of opinion between participants when making different types of decisions. With regard to everyday decisions, there was a 50-50 split between quite often and not very often. Differences of opinion seem to be encountered fairly commonly at the three other levels, with over 80% of respondents (15) encountering them very often or quite often in relation to choices with both short and long term implications. This dropped to 60% (11) in the case of decisions with legal implications, although 4 people gave "don't know" responses to this question. Strategies for resolving such differences were relatively few: review meetings, individual negotiations, prior planning and honesty and understanding were mentioned by some respondents.

These responses, though on a small scale, indicate that there is little consistent practice regarding the involvement of others in the process of decision making. It is of particular concern that in an issue which is so fundamentally concerned with communication, there appears to be limited participation by SLTs. It is unclear from this survey what motivates involvement or the lack of it. We have suggested that access to services is likely to play a major role, but other factors such as relationships between professionals, models of service delivery and the conceptualisation of the decision making process could also feature. It is also apparent that differences of opinion are encountered quite commonly at all levels of decision making.

1.5 Service user participation

Respondents were asked to categorise their current practice for involving service users at different levels of ability in the decision making process. Table 2 shows the rank order of responses in the different categories.

The responses suggest that the practice of inviting service users to reviews is quite widespread, (mentioned by 60% of respondents) although less so for individuals who are likely to actively disengage from the process (33% of respondents). At every level of ability, the strategies for determining choice which are most used appear to be consultation with others, and observation of behaviour (70 - 100% of respondents). Asking service users for their views was a less common practice, even where there was evidence that they could participate (50-60%); predictably and perhaps realistically, this was not a preferred option where service users were passive, or actively disengaging. Around half of the respondents indicated that they would inform the service user about the decision after it was made, a strategy that may be realistic for people with a high anxiety level, or who find decision making difficult – however, this strategy was reported to be used with almost equal frequency with individuals who could and could not actively participate. Advocates were only consulted on average by 39% of respondents, and this does not seem to be influenced by ability level. A consistent small percentage of respondents were likely to use their own judgement without consulting others. When their responses were compared with those of the preceding question, it was evident that in one or two cases, this might be because of a lack of involvement of other people in the decision making process. However, in other cases, there was evidence that reliance on own judgement co-existed with a high level of participation from carers, advocates and other professionals.

Once again, responses to this question suggest that there is wide variation in the practice of decision making. In a substantial number of cases, service users may not be asked their views or invited to meetings. Although this is a very small, self selected sample, the pattern of responses also suggests limited discrimination in practice between service users at different levels of ability: respondents often ticked the same strategies across all groups.

1.6 Process of decision making

In this section, respondents were asked about procedures for making decisions. Seventeen people completed this section.

● *Preparation for meetings*

Half the respondents routinely prepared service users for meetings, by prior discussion, perhaps with symbols, writing down what the user wanted, gathering information, showing people the room, explaining the purpose of the meeting, and building confidence (means unspecified). Six respondents said that whether or not someone was prepared varied depending on the person, and 2 respondents did not usually prepare individuals for meetings. Asked about other ways of preparing for meetings, 8 respondents usually did this. They mentioned anticipating the issues, avoidance of jargon, organisation of the room, and having a prepared format. Five respondents did not usually prepare in other ways, and for 3, it depended on the person.

● *During and after meetings.*

Around half the respondents (7) reported that they usually tried to enable the user to become actively involved in the meeting, whereas for 8 respondents it depended on the person. Two respondents did not usually try to do this (it may not, of course, have been their designated role). Only two or three ways of doing this were mentioned – for example avoidance of jargon, inviting contributions and use of photographs or videos. After the meeting, half the respondents (7) would usually discuss what had happened with the service user, and for half it depended on the person; only one respondent would not usually do this (again, it may not have been the appropriate role). The final question in this section related to record keeping, completed by 16 respondents.(see Table 3). Where respondents left sections blank, this was taken as the equivalent to "rarely or never" on the basis that they had ticked what they did do, and omitted to tick what they did not do. The most common practice is written notes taken as the discussion is ongoing, followed by verbal and/or written reports. For the majority, it is rare for no record of any kind to be kept. However, transcripts, tape and video are very rarely used.

Again, there is a fair amount of variation in reported practice in preparation and conduct of meetings in this group of practitioners. On the face of it, it would seem good practice to take active steps to prepare, involve, and debrief all service users who attend meetings, but it must be emphasised that more information is needed about the contexts of meetings and the roles of different professionals before concluding that this is not routinely happening in the sample. With regard to record keeping, both anecdotal evidence and the reported evidence in this survey of the possibility of differences of opinion would suggest that it is critical to record the outcome of discussions, preferably at the time – and it is clear that this is happening to a large extent. However, when decisions with long term or legal implications are involved, it might be sensible, despite the time involved, to keep some kind of verbatim record so that the evidence of what people say or do is preserved in its entirety. For example, tape recordings or videos could be made and archived for a period of time, without necessarily being transcribed.

1.7 Interpreting the wishes of service users

Finally, respondents were asked for some qualitative information about their views on the process of interpretation. The main problems were felt to be the users' limited ability to engage in conversation; conflict between different interpretations; the time needed to check interpretations out; the levels of challenging behaviour and lack of experience of life events by service users. Respondents relied on signs of pleasure or displeasure, positive engagement, and negative evidence such as a lack of challenging behaviour to confirm or disconfirm their interpretations. The majority of respondents (14) usually tried to check out interpretations, for example by discussions with others; for 2 respondents this varied depending on the person, and one respondent did not usually check out interpretations. The last question asked about ways in which respondents would like to develop the decision making process in their services, and this elicited a wide range of ideas: more involvement and empowerment of service users; staff training in areas such as observation skills, ways of promoting choice and the use of communication aids; involvement of advocates; training for service users in relevant skills; the minimising of factors such as local politics and resource implications; increase in time and clearer definition of areas of responsibility. It is clear that respondents saw that the process of decision making is influenced by a very complex set of factors operating at different levels within organisations. One respondent commented that one of the main problems was that "People interpret within the framework and within the possibilities of their service" – a corroboration of the premise, fundamental to the *See What I Mean* programme, that interpretations always take place in a context, and involve degrees of presupposition and inference.

1.8 Conclusion

The findings of this small scale survey suggest that there is in fact considerable variation in practice, and substantial concern among practitioners. This suggests that a programme is needed which will tackle the issues at a fundamental level, before change can be effected.

Table 1: Participation in decision making

Front line staff/key workers (n= 18)

Very likely	Quite likely	Not very likely	Unknown
Everyday decisions	1	7	1
Choices resulting in short term change	1	4	4
Choices resulting in long term change	8	5	5
Choices with legal implications	5	5	8

Parents or carers (n=18)

Very likely	Quite likely	Not very likely	Unknown
Everyday decisions	9	3	6
Choices resulting in short term change	9	6	3
Choices resulting in long term change	12	1	5
Choices with legal implications	12		6

Senior managers within the service (n=17)

Very likely	Quite likely	Not very likely	Unknown
Everyday decisions	1	2	14
Choices resulting in short term change	3	6	8
Choices resulting in long term change	11	5	2
Choices with legal implications	13	3	11

Independent advocates (n=17)

Very likely	Quite likely	Not very likely	Unknown
Everyday decisions	1	3	121
Choices resulting in short term change	2	5	92
Choices resulting in long term change	5	5	5
Choices with legal implications	8	3	5

Speech and Language therapist (n=17)

Very likely	Quite likely	Not very likely	Unknown
Everyday decisions	2	7	8
Choices resulting in short term change	2	6	9
Choices resulting in long term change	3	5	9
Choices with legal implications	2	4	11

Other outside agencies (eg. social worker, psychologist, GP, solicitor) (n=18)

Very likely	Quite likely	Not very likely	Unknown
Everyday decisions	2	1	15
Choices resulting in short term change	3	9	6
Choices resulting in long term change	11	4	3
Choices with legal implications	12	2	3

Table 2: Strategies for involving service users in decision making

Service users who can actively participate

observe their behaviour in relevant situations	(15)
ask other people what they think	(15)
invite to meeting/case conference/review	(11)
ask the service users to tell you their views	(11)
involve an independent advocate	(6)
inform the service user about the decision after it is made	(6)
rely on your own knowledge of the person without consultation	(5)

Service users who can only participate in a limited way

ask other people what they think	(18)
observe their behaviour in relevant situations	(16)
invite to meeting/case conference/review	(11)
ask the service users to tell you their views	(9)
inform the service user about the decision after it is made	(8)
involve an independent advocate	(7)
rely on your own knowledge of the person without consultation	(4)

Service users who are likely to be passive observers only

ask other people what they think	(18)
observe their behaviour in relevant situations	(15)
invite to meeting/case conference/review	(10)
inform the service user about the decision after it is made	(9)
involve an independent advocate	(7)
rely on your own knowledge of the person without consultation	(5)
ask the service users to tell you their views	(5)

Service users who are likely to actively disengage from the decision making process

ask other people what they think	(14)
observe their behaviour in relevant situations	(13)
inform the service user about the decision after it is made	(8)
involve an independent advocate	(8)
invite to meeting/case conference/review	(6)
rely on your own knowledge of the person without consultation	(4)
ask the service users to tell you their views	(2)

Table 3: Records of meetings

	Usually	Sometimes	Only rarely or never
Video recording	0	1	15
Tape recording	0	1	15
Written transcript (ie writing down exactly what is said while the discussion is going on)	2	4	10
Written notes taken as the discussion is going on	14		2
Full report written after the discussion	8	3	5
Notes written after the discussion	4	3	9
Verbal report to manager or significant other	9	3	4
No formal record kept	1		15
Other (please specify)	0	0	0

References

Ashton, G & Ward, A (1992) *Mental Handicap and the Law*, London: Sweet & Maxwell

Bates, E., Benigni, L., Camaioni, L., & Volterra, V. (1979). *The Emergence of Symbols: Cognition and Communication in Infancy*. New York: Academic Press.

Camaioni, L. (1993). The development of intentional communication: a re-analysis. In L. Nadel & L. Camaioni (Eds.), *New Perspectives in Early Communication Development* London: Routledge.

Coupe, J., & Goldbart, J. (1998). *Communication before Speech*. London: David Fulton.

Crossley, R. (1977) Remediation of communication problems through facilitated communication training: A case study. *European Journal of Disorders of Communication*, 32, 61-69

Dennett, D. (1987). *The Intentional Stance*. Cambridge, MA: MIT Press.

Downs, C. & Craft, A. (1997) *Sex in Context: Setting up a Personal and Social Development Programme for Children and Adults with Profound and Multiple Impairments*. Brighton: Pavilion Publishing

Felce, D. (1994) Facilitated communication: results from a number of recently published evaluations. *British Journal of Learning Disabilities*, 22, 122-126.

Grove, N., Porter, J., Bunning, K. & Olsson, C. (1999) Interpreting the meaning of communication by people with severe and profound intellectual disabilities: Theoretical & methodological issues. *Journal of Applied Research in Intellectual Disabilities, 12 (no. 3)* 190-203

Hastings, R. (1996) Does facilitated communication free imprisoned minds? *The Psychologist*, January 1996, 19-24.

Money, D., Collins, G. (1999). Satisfaction for all: a framework for assessing life satisfaction for all people with learning disabilities. *British Journal of Learning Disabilities*, 27, 52-57.

Stamp, G. H., & Knapp, M. L. (1990). The construct of intent in interpersonal communication. *Quarterly Journal of Speech*, 76, 282-299.

Resources

Talking Mats - *A low-tech framework to help people with severe communication difficulties express their views.*

Talking Mats is a framework which uses picture symbols to help people with severe communication difficulties communicate about particular issues relevant to them. It has potential for a wide range of people, both children and adults. It provides them with a means of expressing their views more easily and is an approach which may help them to think about issues in a different way. The package includes a booklet explaining how to use the mats, as well as several pages of examples to get you started. There is also a video accompanying the booklet which shows how three people used the Talking Mats.

AAC Research Team, Department of Psychology
University of Stirling, Stirling, FK9 4LA Scotland
Telephone 01786 467645 Fax 01786 467641
email joan.murphy@stir.ac.uk

In Control? - *Developing guidelines for decision making by people with learning difficulties who have high support needs.*

This project is exploring ways of involving people with learning disabilities in decision making.

James Edge, Values into Action
Oxford House, Derbyshire Street London E2 6HG
Telephone 020 7729 5436

The Putney Auditory Comprehension Screening Test (PACST) - G. Beaumont and J. Marjoribanks.

This test has been developed with residents of the Royal Hospital for Neurodisability, London, with diagnosis of multiple sclerosis, stroke or traumatic brain injury. It may have applications for people with learning disabilities. The test is described in *Brain Injury* 1999, 13(2) 99-112.

Choice Discovered - *Made by Mental Health Media for the Foundation for People with Learning Disabilities.*

A video training resource about communicating with people with severe, multiple and profound learning disabilities, building relationships and supporting people to make choices. The video is accompanied by backup materials for trainers including workshop activities and suggestions for further resources.

Julie Ballard, Sales and Promotions Manager
Foundation for People with Learning Disabilities
21 Cornwall Terrace, London NW1 4QL
020 7535 7400, Fax 020 7535 7474, Website www.mentalhealth.org.uk.

Affective Communication Assessment - J. Coupe, L. Barton, M. Barber, L. Collins, D. Levy and D. Murphy. Manchester: Melland School 1985.

This assessment offers a systematic profile of positive and negative responses to sensory stimuli. Available from Melland High School, Holmcroft Road, Gorton, Manchester M18 7NG

Multimedia Profiling *Acting up*

Acting up is an organisation which has been developing approaches to individual profiles using a range of media including stills, video, sound, graphics and text. People with communication difficulties are actively involved in gathering and selecting the information and sharing it with others. Profiling uses a person-centred approach to build up a picture of a person's past and present life, their personality and how they communicate, their likes and dislikes and the people in their lives.

For further information, contact *Acting up*,
90 De Beauvoir Road, London N1 4EN Telephone 020 7275 9173 Fax 020 7254 8990
Email acting-up@geo2.poptel.org.uk Website www.acting-up.org.uk

Book and Articles

Brown H., Egan-Sage E., Barry G. and McKay C. - (1996) *Towards better interviewing: A handbook for police officers and social workers.* Brighton: Pavilion Publishing.

Holman A. - (1995) Time to decide 'Who decides'. *Community Living* July/August 1998
A short article exploring issues of consent and learning disability.

Jackson E. and Jackson N - (1999) *Helping people with a learning disability explore choice*
London: Jessica Kingsley

Langridge, K. - (1999) The West Cheshire Project. *PMLD Link*, 11, 3, 7-9
The Law Commission - (1995) *Mental Capacity* Paper No. 231. HMSO

Law Society and the BMA - (1995) *Assessment of mental capacity - guidance for doctors and lawyers.* London: BMA.

Parmenter T. R. - (1999) The choice questionnaire: a scale to assess choices excercised by adults with intellectual disability. *Journal of Intellectual and Developmental Disabilities* 24, 107-132.

Parsons M. - (1997) Assisting older adults with severe disabilities in expressing leisure preferences: A protocol for determining choice making skills. *Research in Developmental Disabilities*, 18, 113-126.